BEST OF RIHANNA

FOR PIANO, VOICE & GUITAR

WISE PUBLICATIONS
part of The Music Sales Group
London / New York / Paris / Sydney / Copenhagen / Berlin / Madrid / Hong Kong / Tokyo

Published by
Wise Publications
14-15 Berners Street, London W1T 3LJ, UK.

Exclusive Distributors:
Music Sales Limited
Distribution Centre, Newmarket Road,
Bury St Edmunds, Suffolk IP33 3YB, UK.

Music Sales Pty Limited
20 Resolution Drive,
Caringbah, NSW 2229, Australia.

Order No. AM1004817
ISBN: 978-1-78038-576-1

Edited by Jenni Norey.
Cover designed by Lizzie Barrand.

Printed in the the EU.

Forget sugarcane – Rihanna is Barbados' biggest export, with sales of over 15 million albums worldwide. Officially the highest charting and most successful Bajan artist of all time, the small town girl with obscenely big dreams broke out of her island idyll to become a global superstar.

From teen beauty pageant winner to revenge-wreaking gangsta princess, Robyn Rihanna Fenty has tried several variations of the 'good girl gone bad' image. Criticised as a purveyor of lightweight pop by some but hailed as a rare R&B diva-with-Caribbean-roots by others, Rihanna has stated that her personal goal is to be 'the black Madonna'. Combining tough and vulnerable, R&B and pop, Rihanna walks the line between provocateur and victim.

Back home her grandmother used to call her Rebel Flower and the nickname still fits. They even tweaked it to Reb'l Fleur when naming the fragrance she endorsed. What's more, in her bid for world domination, Rihanna has also stepped up her efforts to create her own fashion line – according to rumours, a modern take on military-inspired chic – and has also diversified into art, releasing a book of photography entitled *The Last Girl On Earth.*

CALIFORNIA KING BED

Words & Music by Jermaine Jackson, Priscilla Hamilton,
Andrew Harr & Alexander Delicata

G/B
Csus2
G5
3fr
D/F#
Lips that felt just like the in - side of a rose.
cur - tains drawn and a lit - tle last night on those sheets.
So
Em
C
how come when I reach out my fing - ers it feels like more than dis - tance be - tween
2º seems
G/B
D
G
D/F#
Em
us?*
In this Ca - li - for - nia king bed we're ten thou - sand miles a - part.
C
G
D/F#
I've been Ca - li - for - nia wish - ing on these stars,

1.
Em
Csus2
Gsus2
for your heart for me. My Ca-li-for-nia King.
2.
G
D/F♯
Em
C
G
D/F♯
Em
C

G
D/F#
8vb till *
Just when I felt like giv - in' up on us you turn a - round and give me one last touch.
G/B
C
Em7
D
That made ev - 'ry - thing feel bet - ter. And e - ven then my eyes got wet - ter.
Cadd9
* So con - fused, wan - na ask you if you love me but I don't wan - na seem so weak.
D/F#
G
Am7
G/B
C
May - be I've been Ca - li - for - nia dream - ing. Yeah.

N.C.
G
D/F#
In this Ca - li - for - nia king bed we're ten
2° Instrumental ad lib.
Em
C
G
thou - sand miles a - part.
I've been Ca - li - for - nia wish -
D/F#
Em
1.
C
- ing on these stars, for your heart for me.
My Ca - li - for - nia King
2.
C
3.
Csus2
G
In this
My Ca - li - for - nia King.

CHEERS (DRINK TO THAT)

Words & Music by Avril Lavigne, Lauren Christy, Scott Spock, Graham Edwards, Jermaine Jackson, Robyn Fenty, Andrew Harr, Corey Gibson, Laura Pergolizzi & Stacy Barthe

E
D
A
Don't let the bas - tards get you down.
Turn it a-round with an-oth - er round.
E
D
A
E
There's a par-ty at the bar ev-'ry - bod-y put your glass-es up and I drink to that,
D
A
E
I drink to that.
E
Dmaj7
A
1. Life's too short to be sit-ting 'round mis - 'ra - ble. And
(2.) hop on the bar, put it all on my card to-night, yeah. Might be

E
Dmaj7
A
peo-ple gon-na talk wheth-er you do-ing bad or good,
yeah.
Got a
mad in the morn-ing but you know we go-ing hard to-night.
It's get-ting
E
Dmaj7
A
drink on my mind and my mind on my mon-ey,
yeah.
Coy-o-te Ugly up in here, no Ty-ra.
It's on-ly
E
Dmaj7
A
Look-ing so bomb, gon-na find me a hon-ey.
up from here, no down-ward spi-ral.
Got my

E
Dmaj7
A
Ray - bans on and I'm feel - ing hel - la cool to - night,
yeah.
E
Dmaj7
A
Ev - 'ry - bod - y's vib - ing so don't no - bod - y start a fight,
yeah.
E
Dmaj7
A
Cheers to the freak - ing week - end. I drink to that, yeah, yeah.

E
D
A
Oh, let the Ja - me - son sink in. I drink to that, yeah, yeah.
Don't let the bas - tards get you down. Turn it a-round with an-oth - er round.
There's a par - ty at the bar ev-'ry - bod - y put your glass - es up and I drink to that,

E
D
A
E
I drink to that.
1.
2.
D
A
E
2.'Bout to
And I drink to that,
D
A
E
I drink to that.

N.C.
Cheers to the freak - ing week - end. I drink to that, yeah, yeah.
D
A
Oh, let the Ja - me - son sink in. I drink to that, yeah, yeah.
E
D
A
Don't let the bas - tards get you down. Turn it a-round with an - oth - er round.
E
D
A
There's a par - ty at the bar ev - 'ry - bod - y put your glass - es up and I drink to that,

E
D
A
E
I drink to that.
D
A
E
D
A
And I drink to that,
I drink to that,
E
E
and I drink to that.
D
A
E
D
A
Repeat to fade

LOVE THE WAY YOU LIE, PART II

Words & Music by Marshall Mathers, Holly Brook & Grant Alexander

E♭
B♭
F
-ed schemes_ and you_ take that_ to new_ ex - tremes._ But you'll
Gm
E♭
B♭
al - ways be_ my he - ro_ e - ven though_ you've lost_ your mind._
F
Gm
E♭
_ Just gon - na stand there and watch me_ burn,_ but that's all_ right_
B♭
F
Gm
_ be-cause_ I like_ the way_ it hurts._ Just gon - na stand there and hear me_ cry,_
6fr
3fr

E♭
B♭
F
but that's all right be-cause I love the way you lie.
I love the way you lie.
Gm
E♭
B♭
Oh,
I love the way you lie.
F
Gm
E♭
2. Now there's gra - vel in our voic - es, glass - es shat -
B♭
F
Gm
- tered from the fight.
In this tug of war, you'll al -

E♭
6fr
B♭
F
N.C.
- ways win__ e - ven when__ I'm right.__ 'Cause you feed__
Gm
3fr
E♭
6fr
B♭
__ me fa - bles from__ your hand__ with vio-lent words__ and emp-
F
Gm
3fr
E♭
6fr
- ty threats._ And it's sick that all__ these bat - tles__ are what__ keeps__
B♭
F
Gm
3fr
__ me sat - is - fied.__ Just gon - na stand there and watch me__ burn,__

E♭
6fr
B♭
F
but that's all right be-cause I like the way it hurts.
Just gon-na
Gm
3fr
E♭
6fr
B♭
stand there and hear me cry,
but that's all right be-cause I love the way you lie.
F
Gm
3fr
E♭
6fr
I love the way you lie.
Oh,
I love the way you lie.
B♭
F
F
Oh.
So may-be I'm a

Gm
3fr
B♭
Gm
3fr
ma-so-chist. I try to run, but I don't wan-na e-ver leave
F
Gm
3fr
B♭
F
till the walls are go-ing up in smoke with all our mem-o-ries. This
Gm
3fr
E♭
6fr
morn-ing, you wake, a sun ray hits your face. Smeared make-up as we lay in the wake of des-truc-tion. Hush ba-by,
B♭
F
speak soft-ly, tell me I'll be sor-ry that you pushed me in - to the cof-fee ta-ble last night so I can push you off me.

Gm
3fr
E♭
6fr
Try and touch me so I can scream at you not to touch me. Run out the room and I'll fol-low you like a lost pup-py.
B♭
F
Ba-by, with-out you, I'm noth-ing, I'm so lost, hug me. Then tell me how ug-ly I am, but that you'll al-ways love me.
Gm
3fr
E♭
6fr
Then af-ter that, shove me, in the af-ter-math of the des-truc-tive path that we're on, two psy-cho-paths. But we
B♭
F
N.C.
know that no mat-ter how man-y knives we put in each oth-er's backs that we'll have each oth-er's backs. 'Cause we're that luck y.

Gm
3fr
E♭
6fr
To-geth-er we move moun- tains, let's not make_ moun-tains out of mole hills. You hit me twice, yeah, but who's count-ing?
B♭
I may have hit you three times,__ I'm start - ing to lose count. But
F
Gm
3fr
to-geth- er, we'll live for-ev- er, we found the youth foun tain. Our love is cra-zy, we're nuts,- but I re-fused couns-'ling.
E♭
6fr
This house is too huge, if you move out I'll burn all two thou - sand

B♭
square feet of it to the ground. Ain't sh** you can do a - bout it.
F
'Cause with you I'm in my f*** - in' mind, with - out you, I'm out it.
Just gon - na
Gm
3fr
E♭
6fr
B♭
stand there and watch me burn, but that's all right be-cause I like the way it hurts.
F
Gm
3fr
E♭
6fr
Just gon - na stand there and hear me cry, but that's all right

B♭
F
because I love the way you lie.
I love the way you lie.
Gm
3fr
E♭
6fr
B♭
I love the way you lie.
F
Gm
3fr
E♭
6fr
I love the way you lie.
B♭
F
N.C.
I love the way you lie.

DISTURBIA

Words by Christopher Brown, Robert Allen & Andre Merritt
Music by Brian Seals

can't e - ven get it start - ed. Noth - ing heard, noth - ing said, can't e - ven speak a - bout it.
it's like they talk - ing to me. Dis - con - nect - ing your call. Your phone don't e - ven ring.
All my life on my head, don't wan - na think a - bout it. Feels like I'm go - ing in - sane.
I got - ta get out or fi - gure this sh** out. It's too close for com -
Yeah.
- fort. Oh.
Bm
D
A
G
It's a thief in the night to come and grab you.
It can creep up in - side you and com - sume you.
A di - sease of the mind,

A G Bm D A G
it can con - trol you. It's too close for com - fort.
2° I feel like a mons - ter.
Throw on your
Bm D A G Bm D
brake - lights. We're in the cit - y of won - der. Ain't gon' play nice, watch out, you
A G Bm D A G
might just go un - der. Bet - ter think twice, your train of thought will be al - tered. So
Bm D A G Bm D
if you must fal - ter be wise. Your mind's in Dis - tur - bi - a. It's like the

A G Bm D A G
dark - ness is the light. Dis - tur - bi - a. Am I scar - ing you to - night? Dis-
Bm D A G Bm D
-tur - bi - a. Ain't used to what you like. Dis - tur - bi - a. Dis-
A G
To Coda N.C.
-tur - bi - a. (Bam bam be dam bam bam be dam bam.
Vocal ad lib.
Em7 D/F#
Bam bam be dam bam bam be dam bam.) Re - lease me from this curse I'm in.

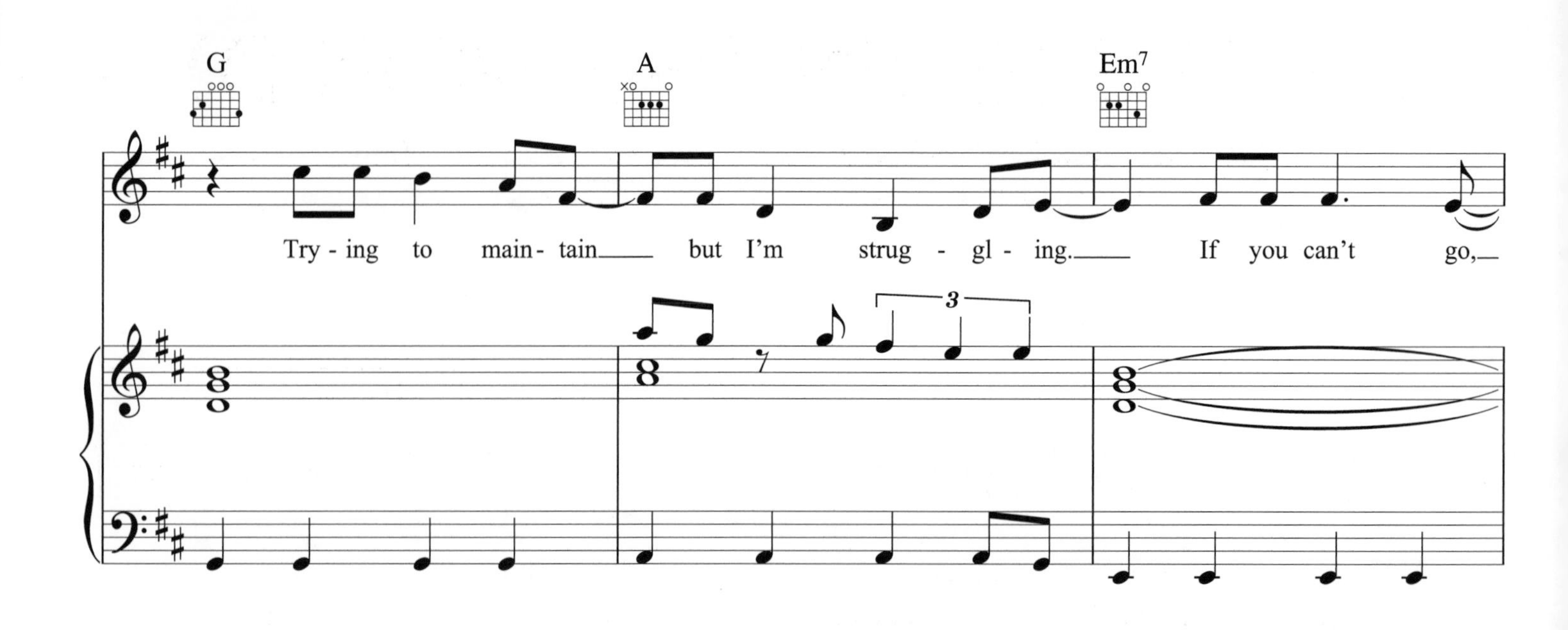
G
A
Em7
Try - ing to main - tain but I'm strug - gl - ing. If you can't go,
3

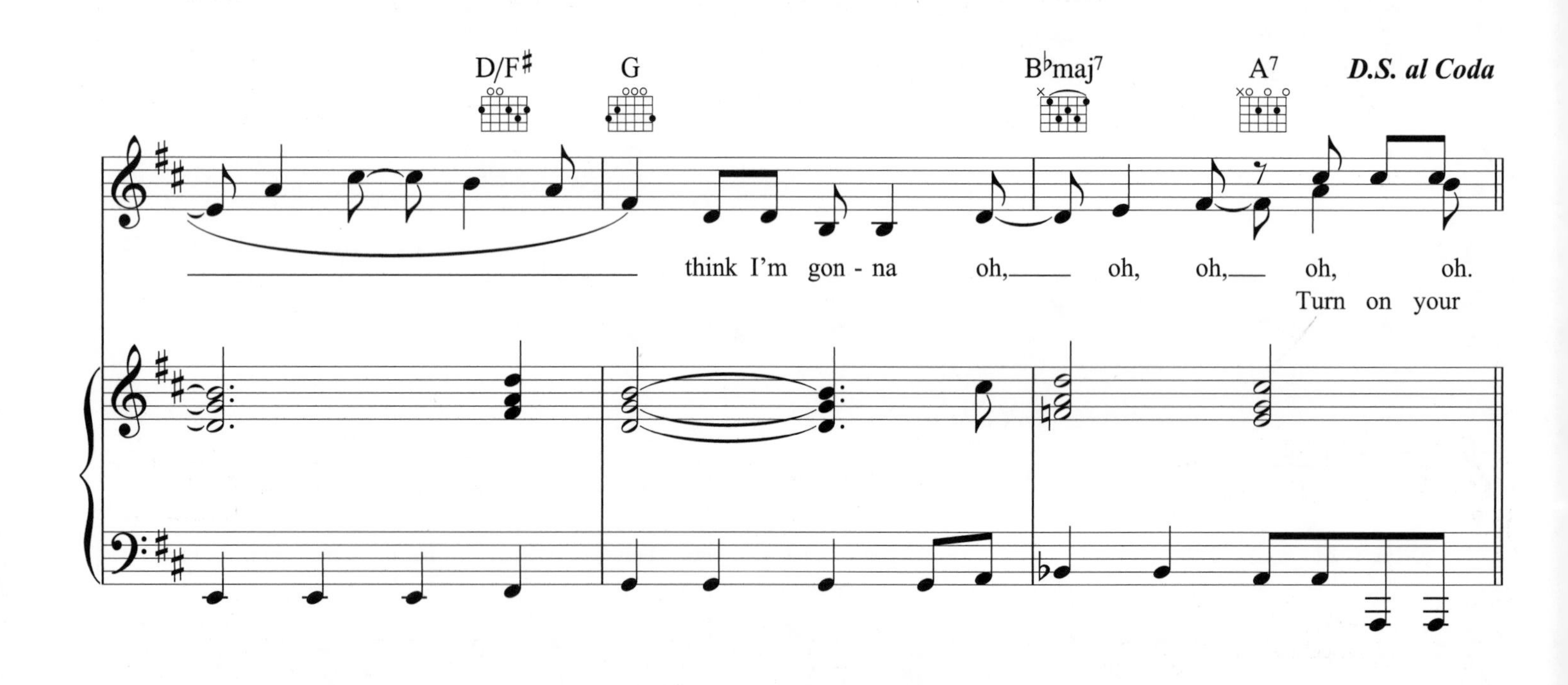
D/F♯
G
B♭maj7
A7
D.S. al Coda
think I'm gon - na oh, oh, oh, oh, oh.
Turn on your

Coda
N.C.
(Bam bam be dam bam bam be dam bam. Bam bam be dam bam bam be dam bam.)
Vocal ad lib.

ONLY GIRL (IN THE WORLD)

WORDS & MUSIC BY CRYSTAL JOHNSON, MIKKEL S. ERIKSEN,
TOR ERIK HERMANSEN & SANDY WILHELM

So boy, for - get a - bout the world 'cause it's gon' be me and you to - night.
Ba - by, I'll tell you all my se - crets that I'm keep - ing; you can come in - side.
8vb
I wan - na make you beg for it and then I'll make you swal - low your pride.
And when you en - ter you ain't leav - in', be my pri - son - er for the night.
8vb
G
Oh. Want you to make me feel like I'm the on - ly girl in the world.
Bm
G
Like I'm the on - ly one that you'll ev - er love. Like I'm the on - ly one who knows your heart.

Bm
G
On - ly girl in the world.
Like I'm the
Bm
on - ly one that's in command.
'Cause I'm the on - ly one who un - der - stands
G
To Coda II
Em
To Coda I
F♯m
G
how to make you feel like a man.
Yeah.
2º like I'm the on - ly one who knows your heart.
On -
G
Want you to make me feel like I'm the on - ly girl in the world.

Bm
G
Like I'm the on - ly one that you'll ev - er love.
Like I'm the
Em
F♯m
G
D.S. al Coda I
on - ly one who knows your heart.
On - ly one.
2. Want you to
Coda I
G
D
A
Bm
- ly one.
Take me for a ride, ride.
Oh,
ba - by take me high, high.
Let me make you burst, burst.
Oh,

1.
2.
D
A
Bm
Bm
D.S.S. al Coda II
make it last all night, night.
night.
Want you to
Coda II
Em
F#m
G
On - ly girl in the world.
Bm
Girl in the world.
On - ly girl in the world.
G
Em
F#m
G
Girl in the world.
8vb

RUDE BOY

Words & Music by Mikkel S. Eriksen, Tor Erik Hermansen, Makeba Riddick,
Esther Dean, Rob Swire & Robyn Fenty

E♭m
B♭m
C♭
A♭m
B♭m
6fr
4fr
Come here rude boy, boy can you get it up?
Come here rude boy, boy is you big e-nough?
Take it, take it, ba-by, ba-by. Take it, take it, love me, love me.
1. To-night I'm-a let you be the cap-tain. To-night I'm-a let you do your thing, yeah.
2. To-night I'm-a give it to you hard-er. To-night I'm-a turn your bod-y out.
To-night I'm-a let you be a ri-der. Gid-dy up, gid-dy up, gid-dy up, babe.
Re-lax, let me do it how I wan-na. If you got it, I need it and I'm-a put it down.

A♭m
4fr
B♭m
To - night I'm - a let it be fire.
Buck-le up, I'm - a give it to you strong - er.
To - night I'm - a let you take me high - er.
Hands up, we can go a lit - tle long - er.
E♭m
6fr
B♭m
C♭
A♭m
4fr
B♭m
To - night, ba - by, we can get it on, yeah. We can get it on, yeah.
To - night I'm - a get a lit - tle cra - zy. Get a lit - tle cra - zy, babe.
Do you like it boy? I
E♭m
6fr
B♭m
C♭
A♭m
4fr
B♭m
wa - wa - want what you wa - wa - want. Give it to me, ba - by, like boom, boom, boom. What I
E♭m
6fr
B♭m
C♭
A♭m
4fr
B♭m
wa - wa - want is what you wa - wa - want. Na, nah.

E♭m B♭m C♭ A♭m B♭m
6fr 4fr
Come here rude boy, boy can you get it up? Come here rude boy, boy is you big e-nough?
Take it, take it, ba-by, ba-by. Take it, take it, love me, love me.
Come here rude boy, boy can you get it up? Come here rude boy, boy is you big e-nough?
Take it, take it, ba-by, ba-by. Take it, take it, love me, love me.

A♭m
G♭
D♭
E♭m
4fr
6fr
I like the way you touch me there. I like the way you pull my hair.
Babe, if I don't feel it I ain't fak - ing, no, no. (Oh, no!)
I like when you tell me kiss it there. I like when you tell me move it there.
C♭
So gid-dy up. Time to gid-dy up. You say you're a rude boy. Show me what you got now.

N.C.
Come here right now.
Take it, take it, ba - by, ba - by. Take it, take it, love me, love me.
E♭m
6fr
B♭m
C♭
A♭m
4fr
B♭m
Come here rude boy, boy can you get it up?
Come here rude boy, boy is you big e-nough?
E♭m
6fr
B♭m
C♭
A♭m
4fr
B♭m
Take it, take it, ba - by, ba - by. Take it, take it, love me, love me.

E♭m
B♭m
C♭
A♭m
B♭m
6fr
4fr
Come here rude boy, boy can you get it up?
Come here rude boy, boy is you big e - nough?
Take it, take it, ba - by, ba - by. Take it, take it, love me, love me.
Love me, love me. (Love me, love me, love me, love me, love me, love me.)
Take it, take it, ba - by, ba - by. Take it, take it, love me, love me.

RUSSIAN ROULETTE

Words & Music by Shaffer Smith & Charles Harmon

B/F#
D/F#
Bm/F#
(2.)
you play for keeps
to your-self.
Take a gun,
He says "Close your eyes,
and count to three.
some-times it helps."
C#/F#
F#m
Bm/F#
I'm sweat-ing now,
And then I get
mov-ing slow.
a scar-y thought
No time to think,
that he's here
D/F#
C#/F#
F#m
my turn to go.
means he's nev - er lost.
And you can see my
heart
beat-
D
E
Bm
- ing.
You can see it through my
chest.
And I'm ter - ri - fied

F♯m
D
E
but I'm not leav - ing.
I know that I must pass this test
1.
Bm
C♯
N.C.
so I just pull the trig - ger.
2. Say a prayer
2.
Bm
C♯
D
A
so I just pull the trig - ger.
As my life flash - es be - fore my eyes I'm
Bm
F♯m
F♯m/E
D
wond - er - ing will I ev - er see an - oth - er sun - rise?
So man - y won't get the
3
3

B/D♯
E
C♯/E♯
C♯
chance to say good-bye but it's too late too pick up the val - ue of my life. And you can see my
F♯m
D
E
heart beat - ing. You can see it through my chest.
Bm
F♯m
D
And I'm ter - ri - fied but I'm not leav - ing. I
E
Bm
C♯
F♯m
know that I must pass this test You can see my heart beat

D
E
Bm
- ing. Oh, you can see it through my chest. And I'm ter - ri - fied
F♯m
D
E
but I'm not leav - ing. I know that I must pass this test
Bm
C♯
N.C.
so I just pull the trig - ger.
Ha - ha - ha - ha. Ha - ha.

TAKE A BOW

Words & Music by Mikkel Eriksen, Tor Erik Hermansen & Shaffer Smith

E
B
C♯m
A
1. You look so dumb right now,
2. Grab your clothes and get gone,
you'd bet-ter hur-ry up,
E
B
C♯m
A
E
B
stand-ing out-side my house.
be-fore the sprink-lers come on.
Try-ing to a-pol-o-gise,
Talk-ing 'bout, "Girl I love you, you're the one."
C♯m
A
E
B/D♯
Dsus2
you're so ug-ly when you cry.
This just looks like a re-run.
Please! Just cut it out.
Please! What else is on?
And
E
B
C♯m
A
Don't tell me you're sor-ry 'cause you're not.
Ba-by, when I

E
B
D
know you're on - ly sor - ry you got caught. But you
E
B
C#m7
Asus2
E
B
put on quite a show, real - ly had me go - ing, but now it's time to go,
C#m7
Asus2
E
B
C#m7
Asus2
cur-tain's fin - al - ly clos - ing. That was quite a show, ver - y en - ter - tain - ing,
F#m7
E/G#
A6
A
E/G#
D
To Coda
but it's o - ver now. Go on and take a bow. Oh.

B/A B C♯m7 F♯m7 E/G♯
4fr
And the award for the best lie goes to you for mak-ing me
B/A B C♯m7 D
believe that you could be faith-ful to me. Let's hear your speech. Oh.
E B C♯m A E B/D♯
How 'bout a round of ap-plause? Stand-ing o-va-
Dsus2
D.S. al Coda
tion? But you
rit.
Coda
F♯m7 E/G♯ A
But it's o-ver now.

TE AMO

Words & Music by Mikkel S. Eriksen, Tor Erik Hermansen,
James Fauntleroy II & Robyn Fenty

G♯m
F♯
D♯m
E
D♯m
F♯
4fr
6fr
I hear the pain in her voice.
I hold her hand, I got no choice.
Then we danced
Pulled me out
G♯m
F♯
D♯m
E
D♯m
un - der - neath the can - de - la - bra, she takes the lead.
on the beach, danced in the wa - ter. I start to leave.
C♯m
B
C♯m
B
F♯
That's when I saw it in her eyes. It's o - ver.
She's beg - ging me and ask - ing why it's o - ver.
Then she said
G♯m
F♯
D♯m
E
D♯m
F♯
"Te a - mo" then she put her hand a-round my waist. I told her no. She cried

G♯m F♯ D♯m E D♯m F♯
4fr 6fr 6fr
"Te a - mo." I told her I'll nev-er run a - way, but let me go. My
G♯m F♯ D♯m E D♯m
4fr 6fr 6fr
soul is a - wry, with - out ask - ing why. I said
C♯m B C♯m B F♯
4fr 4fr
To Coda
"Te a - mo." Wish some-bod-y'd tell me what she said. Don't it mean I love
G♯m F♯ D♯m E D♯m F♯
4fr 6fr 6fr
you? Think it means I love

G♯m F♯ D♯m E D♯m F♯
you. Don't it mean I love
E D♯m E D♯m E F♯
you? Yes, and we can dance but you got - ta watch your hands.
G♯m F♯ G♯m
Watch me all night, I move un-der the light be-cause I un - der - stand
E D♯m E D♯m E B/F♯
that we all need love. And I'm not a - fraid.

C♯m
B
F♯
D.S. al Coda
I feel the love, but I don't feel that way. Then she said
Coda
F♯
G♯m
F♯
D♯m
it mean I love you?
E
D♯m
F♯
G♯m
F♯
D♯m
Think it means I love you.
E
D♯m
F♯
G♯m
F♯
Don't it mean I love you?

D♯m
E
D♯m
Think it means I love
you.
I love you.
C♯m
B
C♯m
B
F♯
"Te a - mo, te a - mo."
Don't it mean I
C♯m
B
C♯m
B
F♯
Free time
N.C.
love you?
G♯m
8vb

UNFAITHFUL

Words & Music by Mikkel Eriksen, Tor Erik Hermansen & Shaffer Smith

Fm/C
A♭
4fr
Fm/A♭
Sor - row in my soul, 'cause it seems that wrong
A kiss up - on my cheek, he's here re - luc - tant - ly. As
A♭maj7
4fr
G7sus4
G7
Cm
3fr
real - ly loves my com - pa - ny.
He's more than a man and
if I'm gon - na be out late
I say I won't be long, just
Fm/C
Cm
3fr
Fm/C
this is more than love. The rea - son that the sky is blue.
But
hang - ing with the girls. A lie I did - n't have to tell,
be - cause
A♭
4fr
Fm/A♭
A♭maj7
4fr
clouds are roll - ing in be - cause I'm gone a - gain and to him I just can't be true.
we both know where I'm a - bout to go and we know it ver - y well.

G7sus4
G7
A♭
B♭
And I know that
'Cause I know that
he knows_ I'm un - faith - ful__ and it
Cm
B♭/D
E♭
A♭
kills him__ in - side to know that I am hap - py__ with
B♭
A♭add9
some oth - er guy.___ I can see him dy - ing,
Cm
A♭
Fm7
I don't wan - na do this an - y - more. I don't wan - na
3fr
4fr
6fr

B♭
Cm
A♭
B♭
be the rea - son why. Ev-'ry-time I walk out the door I see him die a
Fm
Cm
A♭
lit - tle more in - side. I don't wan - na hurt him an - y - more
Fm7
B♭
A♭add9
I don't wan-na take a - way his life. I don't wan - na be
B♭
To Coda
1.
Cm
Fm/C
a mur-der-er.

Cm
Fm/C
2.
A♭
2. I
a mur-der-er.
Our love,
B♭
Cm
B♭/D
E♭
A♭
his trust.
I might as well
take a gun and put it to his head,
B♭
A♭add9
get it o-ver with.
I don't wan-na do this
Cm
A♭
Fm7
B♭
an-y-more.
Oh.

Cm
3fr
A♭
4fr
B♭
D.S. al Coda
An - y - more.
Coda
B♭
Cm
3fr
Fm/C
a mur-der-er.
Cm
3fr
Fm/C
A♭
4fr
A mur-der-er.
Fm/A♭
A♭maj7
4fr
G7sus4
G7
Cm
3fr
No, no, no.
Yeah, yeah.

WE FOUND LOVE

Words & Music by Calvin Harris

D♯m
B
F♯
G♯7no3
6fr
4fr
It's the way I'm feel - ing I just can't_ de -
- ny,
but I've got - ta let it go.
We found love in a hope - less place.
We found love in a hope - less place.

D♯m
B
F♯
G♯7no3
6fr
4fr
Shine a light through an o - pen door.
Love and life I will di - vide.
Turn a-way 'cause I need you more.
F♯
Feel the heart - beat in my mind.

D♯m
B
F♯
G♯7no3
F♯
B
F♯
G♯7no3
6fr
4fr
It's the way I'm feel - ing I just can't de -
D♯m
B
F♯
G♯7no3
D♯m
B
F♯
G♯7no3
- ny, but I've got - ta let it go.
We found love in a hope - less place. We found love in a hope - less place.
D♯m

Yel-low dia - monds in the light
and we're stand - ing side by side as your shad - ow
cross - es mine.
D#m
B
F#
G#7no3
6fr
4fr
We found love in a hope - less place. We found love in a hope - less place.

D♯m
6fr
D♯m
B
F♯
G♯7no3
4fr
D♯m
B
F♯
G♯7no3
D♯m
B
F♯
G♯7no3
D♯m
B
We found love in a hope - less place.
We found love in a
1.
2.
F♯
G♯7no3
F♯
G♯7no3
N.C.
hope - less place.
hope - less place.

WHAT'S MY NAME?

Words & Music by Mikkel S. Eriksen, Tor Erik Hermansen, Traci Hale,
Ester Dean & Aubrey Graham

F♯m
A
Spoken: I heard you good with them soft lips,
yeah, you know word of mouth.
Dmaj7
E
The square root of sixty nine is eight somethin'.
Right? 'Cause I've been tryin' to work it out.
F♯m
A
Dmaj7
Oh, good... white wine.
Oh, I come alive in the night time.
O.K. away we go.
E
F♯m
A
Only thing we have on is the radio.
Oh, let it play.
Say you gotta leave but I know you wanna stay.

Dmaj7
E
You just waiting in the traffic jam to finish, girl.
The things that we could do in twenty minutes, girl.
F♯m
A
Say my name, say my name, wear it out.
It's getting hot, crack a window, air it out.
Dmaj7
E
I could get you through a mighty long day. Soon as
you go, the text that I write gon' say...
Oh,
F♯m
A
na na. What's my name? Oh, na na. What's my name? Oh,

Dmaj7
E
na na. What's my name? What's my name? What's my name?
1. Not ev - 'ry - bod -
2. Ba - by you got
F♯m
A
- y knows how to work my bod - y, knows how to make me want
me and ain't no-where that I'd be than with your arms a - round
Dmaj7
E
it. But boy, you stay up on it. You got that some -
me. Back and forth you rock me, yeah. So I sur - ren -
F♯m
A
- thin' that keeps me so off ba - lance. Ba - by, you're a chal -
- der to ev - 'ry word you whis - per. Ev - 'ry door you en -

Dmaj7
E
- lenge, let's ex - plore your ta - lent. Hey,
- ter I will let you in.
F#m
A
boy, I real - ly wan - na see if you can go down town with a girl like me. Hey,
Dmaj7
E
boy, I real - ly wan - na be with you 'cause you're just my type. Ooh, na na na na.
I need a boy to take it o - ver. Look - in' for a guy to put you un - der.

1, 3.
F#m
Oh.
Oh.
Hey, boy, I real-ly wan-na see if you can
A
Dmaj7
go down town with a girl like me. Hey, boy I real-ly wan-na be with you 'cause you're
E
F#m
just my type. Ooh, na na na na. I need a boy to take it o - ver.
A
Dmaj7
To Coda
E
Look-in' for a guy to put you un - der. Oh.
Oh.
Oh,

D E F#m E/G# A
Oh. You're so a-maz-ing, you took the time to fi-gure me out,
D E F#m E/G# A D E
that's why you take me way past the point of turn-ing me on. You 'bout to break me, I
F#m E/G# A Bm A E/G#
swear you got me los-ing my mind. Oh,
F#m A Dmaj7
na na. What's my name? Oh, na na. What's my name?

E
F♯m
A
Oh, na na. What's my name? Oh, na na. What's my name? Oh,
Dmaj7
E
D.S. al Coda
na na. What's my name? What's my name? What's my name? Hey,
Coda
Dmaj7
E
F♯m
A
Oh.
Dmaj7
E
F♯m

UMBRELLA

Words & Music by Terius Nash, Christopher Stewart, Thaddis Harrell & Shawn Carter

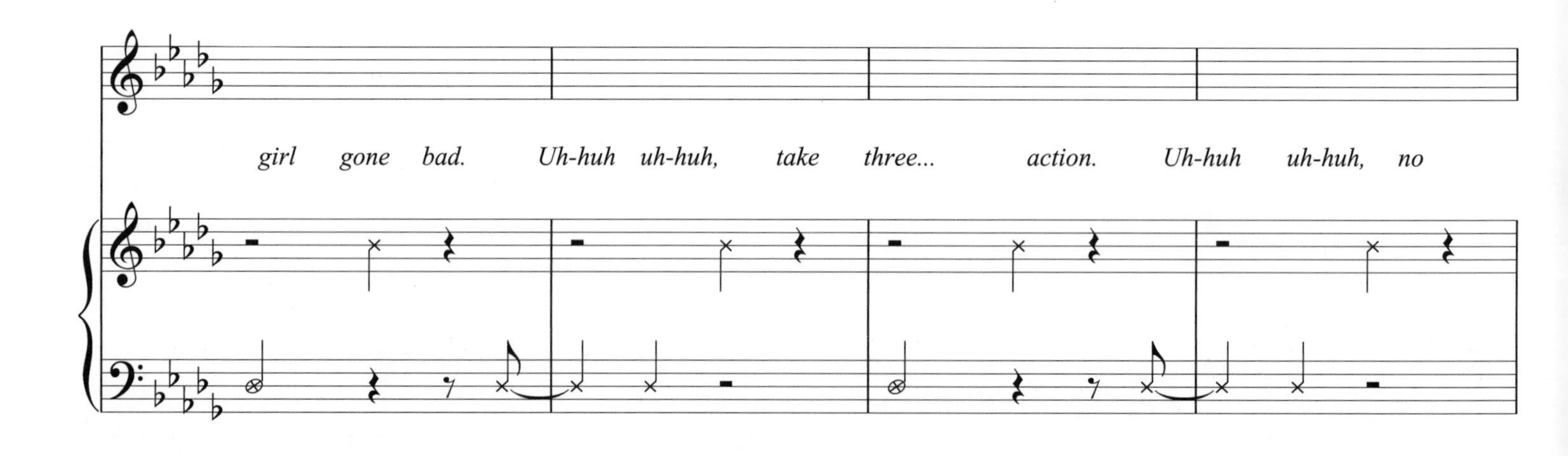

eh eh eh eh.
clouds come we gone, we Rocafella, she fly higher than weather and she rocks it better.
You know me an anticipation for precipitation, stacks chips for the rainy day
Eh eh eh, eh eh eh eh. 1. You
Jay rain man is back with little Ms. Sunshine Rihanna, where you at?
G♭maj7
D♭/A♭
4fr
had my heart, and we'll nev-er be worlds a-part, may - be in
(2.) fan - cy things, will nev-er come in - be - tween; you're part of my

Fm7
B♭m
mag - a - zines, but you'll still be my star. Ba - by, 'cause
en - ti - ty, here for in - fin - i - ty. When the war has
G♭maj7
D♭/A♭
4fr
in the dark, you can see shin - y cars, and that's when you
took its part, when the world has dealt its cards; if the
Fm7
B♭m
need me there; with you I'll al - ways share.
hand is hard, to-geth - er we'll mend your heart.
Be - cause,
G♭maj7
D♭
4fr
when the sun shines we'll shine to - geth - er, told you I'll be here for - ev -
84

A♭
B♭m
-er, said I'll al - ways be your friend, took an oath I'm - a stick it out till the end.
G♭maj7
D♭
Now that it's rain - ing more than ev - er know that we'll still have each oth -
A♭
B♭m
- er. You can stand un - der my um - b - rel - la. You can stand un - der my um - b - rel -
G♭maj7
D♭/A♭
- la, 'el - la, 'el - la, eh eh eh. Un - der my um - b - rel -
4fr

Fm
B♭m
-la, 'el - la, 'el - la, eh eh eh. Un - der my um - b - rel -
G♭maj7
D♭/A♭
4fr
-la, 'el - la, 'el - la, eh eh eh. Un - der my um - b - rel -
Fm
To Coda
B♭m
-la, 'el - la, 'el - la, eh eh eh eh eh eh.
2. These
B
G♭
You can run in - to my arms, it's o - kay don't be a - larmed, come

D♭maj7
4fr
A♭sus4
4fr
in to me; there's no dis - tance in - bet - ween our love.
B
G♭
So gon - na let the rain pour; I'll be all you need and
F9
D.S. al Coda
more. Be - cause,
Coda
B♭7
B♭m
eh eh eh eh eh.
It's

B♭m7
D♭/A♭
4fr
rain - ing, rain - ing. Ooh, ba - by, it's rain - ing, rain - ing. Ba - by, come
A♭
4fr
B♭m
in to me, come in to me. It's
B♭m7
D♭/A♭
4fr
rain - ing, rain - ing. Ooh, ba - by, it's rain - ing, rain - ing. You can al - ways come
A♭
4fr
B♭m
Repeat ad lib. and fade
in to me, come in to me. It's

1 2 3 4 5 6 7 8 9